Contents

CVC words: things

Trace the word for each thing.

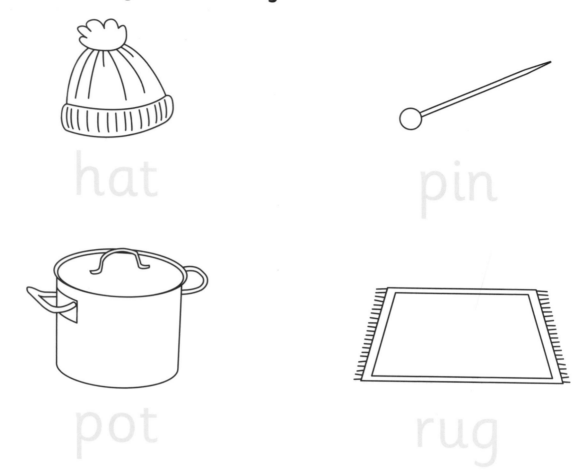

hat

pin

pot

rug

Colour the missing initial letter. Write it below to finish the word.

m l r   j q s

___og   ___un

Schofield & Sims

Writing Words

Literacy

Writing Words

Get Set
Early Years

tent

log

camp

Name

Introduction

The **Get Set** activity books are full of fun activities that help you to reinforce at home the learning that your child is doing at school.

This activity book is about **Writing Words**. It focuses on developing your child's fine motor skills for writing and their understanding of the shapes and movements that are required to write different letters to form words, as well as their ability to encode words to begin to spell. The book falls within the curriculum area of Literacy in the Early Years Foundation Stage (EYFS) framework. This activity book is supported by four other activity books for Literacy: **Reading and Rhyme**, **Letter Sounds**, **Phonics** and **Writing Letters**.

It is recommended that your child starts this activity book in Term 2 of the Reception year, or when your child is already quite confident in their letter formation, completing one or two pages at a time over the remainder of the year. They should complete pages 4 to 9 in Term 2 and pages 10 to 33 in Term 3. As your child works through the book, the tasks will gradually become more challenging, requiring more reading and writing skills, helping to prepare your child for the more formal style of learning that begins in Key Stage 1.

It is worth remembering, however, that children develop and learn in different ways and at different rates, especially at this young age, and you may prefer to work through the books at your child's own pace. The activity books may also be suitable for older or younger children, depending on ability.

Before beginning each activity, read the instructions aloud to your child. Discuss what they can see in the pictures and what they have to do to complete the activity. When supporting your child to write words, the emphasis should be on starting each letter in the correct place and remembering the movements, rather than on size or neatness. It is natural at this age for your child to experiment with and move between a variety of different pencil grips. Try to model and encourage them to hold the pencil between thumb and forefinger, resting it on the third finger, but don't expect them to hold the pencil this way every time.

At the back of the book you will find **Notes for parents and carers**, with helpful guidance relating to each page of the activity book. For each topic, there is a **Teaching tip**, which explains how best to support your child as they complete the activities, **Key vocabulary**, for you to model and encourage your child to use themselves, and a practical **Extension activity**, for you to explore the topic further with your child in a real-life context.

These notes help you to get the most out of the activity books and to support and enhance your child's learning. When working through the activities, don't worry too much about your child 'getting it right'. The emphasis should instead be on 'having a go' and taking the time to enjoy exploring new topics and ideas together.

Published by **Schofield & Sims Ltd**,
7 Mariner Court, Wakefield, West Yorkshire WF4 3FL, UK
Telephone 01484 607080
www.schofieldandsims.co.uk

This edition copyright © Schofield & Sims Ltd, 2018
First published in 2018
Fourth impression 2020

Authors: **Sophie Le Marchand and Sarah Reddaway**
Sophie Le Marchand and Sarah Reddaway have asserted their moral rights under the Copyright, Designs and Patents Act, 1988, to be identified as the authors of this work.

British Library Cataloguing in Publication Data
A catalogue record for this book is available from the British Library.

Design by **Oxford Designers & Illustrators Ltd**
Cover illustration by **Conor Rawson**
Printed in the UK by **Page Bros (Norwich) Ltd**

ISBN 978 07217 1444 8

CVC words: animals

Trace and write the animal names.

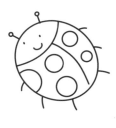  

bug   fox   bat

_____ _____ _____

Unscramble the letters and write the animal names.

tca   enh   gip

_____ _____ _____

odg   ayk   ckud

_____ _____ _____

CVC words: actions

Trace and write the action words.

hop   sit   run

_____   _____   _____

Write the missing letter to finish the action word.

r__p   n__p   __ig

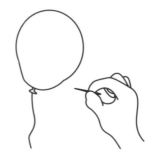

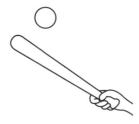

__op   __iss   hi__

CVC words: describing words

Trace and write the describing words.

big   hot   fit

_____   _____   _____

Write the initial letter for each picture. Copy the letters to write a new describing word.

High-frequency words

Draw a ring around the 2-letter words. Write them below.

mum   up

am   it

a   dad   not

_____   _____   _____

Read the high-frequency words. Then cover them and practise writing them.

but   _____   _____

had   _____   _____

and   _____   _____

can   _____   _____

Tricky words

Memorise each tricky word on the first bus. Then cover it and write it on the second bus.

go to

the

Read the tricky word on the bowl. Write it on each scoop of ice cream.

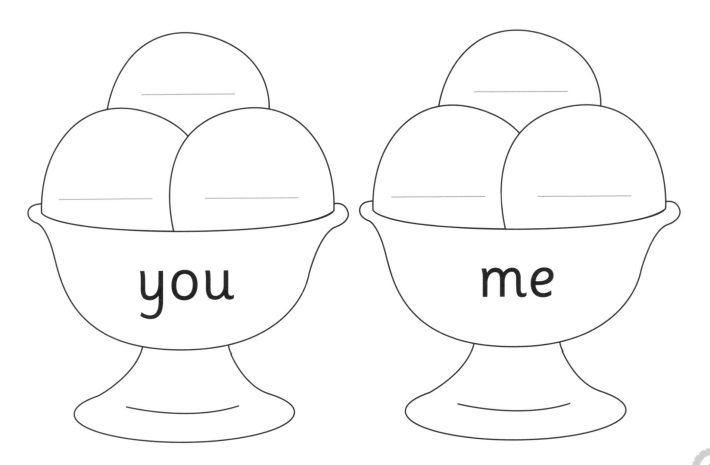

you

me

Words with double letters

Copy the double-letter words as many times as you can.

buzz _____

tell _____

hiss _____

puff _____

Fish for double letters. Draw a ring around each pair and write them in to finish each word.

zz

ss

ff

ll

mi_____

we_____

fi_____

cu_____

More words with double letters

Find and copy the right double-letter word to label each picture.

_____   _____   _____

| **bull** | **jazz** | **kiss** |

Label 4 things in the park that have double letters.

_____

_____

_____

_____

Words with ck

Copy the 'ck' words as many times as you can.

kick _____

back _____

neck _____

ticket _____

Join the dots to find the thing that ends with 'ck'. Write the word below.

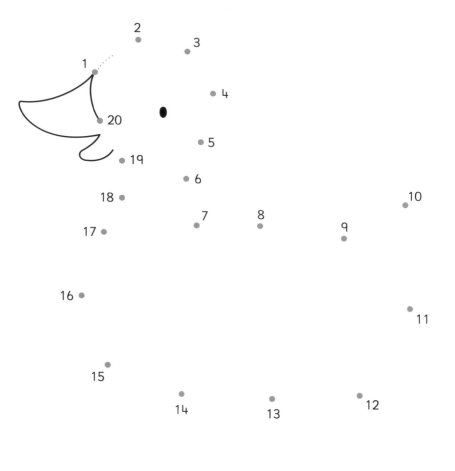

_____

Get Set Literacy

Words with sh and ch

Write 'sh' or 'ch' to finish the words.

_____op

_____ip

fi_____

ri_____

Find and copy the right word to label each picture. Colour the 'sh' pictures red and the 'ch' pictures blue.

shell   bench   chick   ship

Words with th and ng

Copy the 'th' and 'ng' words as many times as you can.

this _____

that _____

thin _____

thick _____

Find and copy an 'ng' word to label each picture.

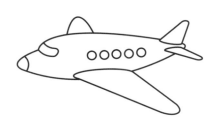

ring   king   sing   wing

Words with ai, ee and igh

Find and copy the right words below the keys to help free the knight from jail.

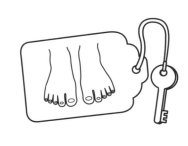

feet   rain   night   paint

Underline the missing letters for each word. Write them in to finish the word.

ai ee igh

b_____

ai ee igh

t____l

ai ee igh

tr_____

ai ee igh

l____t

Words with oa, oo and ar

Find and colour the letter that makes a real word. Write the word below.

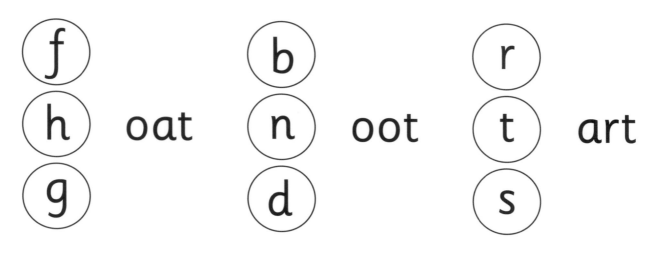

ⓕ
ⓗ oat
ⓖ

ⓑ
ⓝ oot
ⓓ

ⓡ
ⓣ art
ⓢ

Play a game of 'I spy' to spot 'oa', 'oo' and 'ar' words. Write the words for what you find on the lines below.

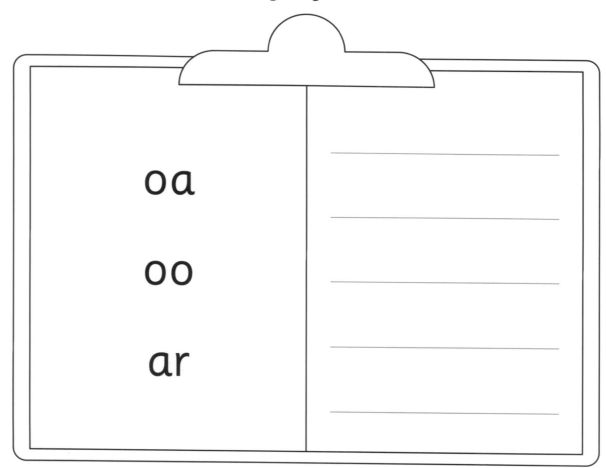

oa

oo

ar

Words with or, ur and ow

Find and copy the right word to label each picture.

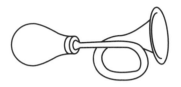

_____

_____

_____

_____

| horn | fork | church | owl |

Write the missing word to finish the sentence.

I can _____  .

The _____  is big.

I see the _____ light.

Words with oi, ear and air

Find and copy the right word to label each picture.

_____

_____

_____

_____

beard   coin   chair   toilet

Write 2 of your own words for 'oi', 'ear' and 'air'.

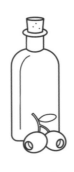

oil

spear

fairy

_____

_____

_____

_____

_____

_____

Words with er and ure

Find and colour the letter that makes a real word. Write the word below.

c

(f) ure

h

g
(h) er
s

j
(m) ure
p

_____   _____   _____

Finish writing the 'er' words.

_____mm_____

_____tt_____

_____tt_____

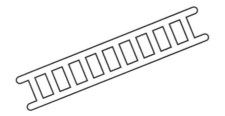

_____dd_____

More high-frequency words

Read it, find it, circle it, write it.

will	see
see	look
that	will
look	that
	look
	see
	will
	that

_____

_____

_____

_____

Help the boy complete the letter triangles for these high-frequency words.

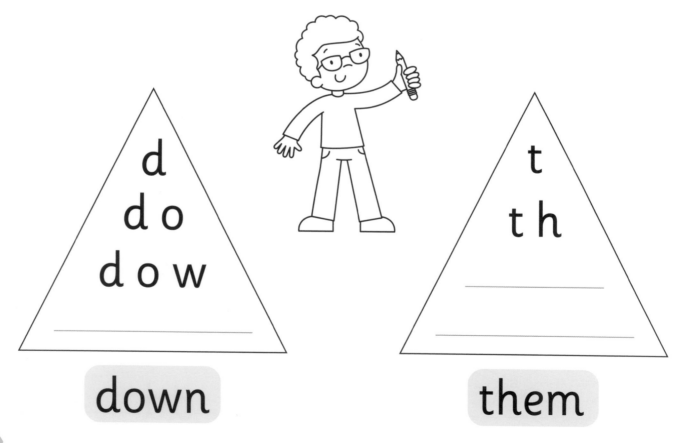

d
d o
d o w
_____

down

t
t h
_____

them

More tricky words

Copy each tricky word on to the matching sea creature.

have

like

you

Copy each tricky word in its lane on the running track. Repeat it up to the end of the lane.

so

one

were

Captions

Think of a simple caption to describe each picture. Write the captions.

Draw your own comic strip story and write captions.

Character captions

Write what each character is saying in the speech bubbles.

Write what each character is thinking in the thought bubbles.

CVCC words: things

Draw a ring around the vowel sound for each picture.
Write the word below.

a e i o u

_____

a e i o u

_____

a e i o u

_____

a e i o u

_____

Write a list of things for sale at the jumble sale.

CVCC words: actions

Write the missing end letters to finish each word.

ju_____

pai_____

be_____

he_____

Work out the missing letter in each word. Write the words below.

m__lt

_____

win__

_____

th__nk

_____

__and

_____

CVCC words: describing words

Find and copy the right word to label each picture.

_____ _____ _____

best   cold   lost

Look at the pictures. Write the word 'soft' or 'fast' below each one.

_____ _____ _____

_____ _____ _____

CCVC words: things

Find and copy the right word to label each picture.

_____

_____

_____

_____

stem   train   dress   pram

Write the missing word to finish the sentence.

I see a _____ 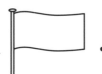 .

I bang the _____  .

The _____ is fun.

CCVC words: animals

Join the dots to find the CCVC-word animal. Write the word on the line.

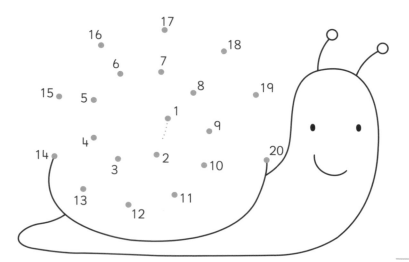

_____

Unscramble each animal name and write the word.

_____

_____

_____

_____

acbr   grof   gtsa   aclm

CCVC words: actions

Find and copy the right action word to label each picture.

_____   _____

_____   _____

spin   step   trip   clap

Write out the shaded letters in the grid to spell out an action word.

f	r	i	t
b	l	u	p

a	r	m	p
d	c	o	x

s	g	v	p
e	t	o	q

_____ _____ _____

Capital letters

Trace the capital letters on the signs.

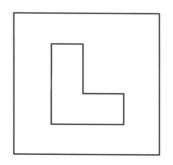 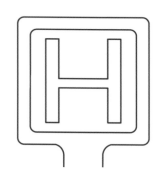 

Trace the capital letters in the children's names. Then write the names below.

Carl

Orla

Meg

Ella

Tim

Max

More capital letters

Trace the words in capital letters on the signs and then read the signs.

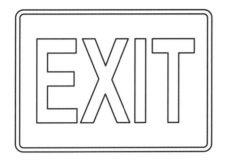

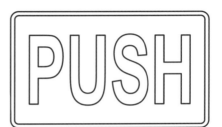

Copy the children's names on to their party invitations.

Mark   Sasha   Oliver

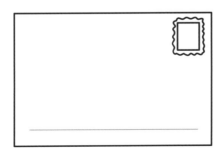

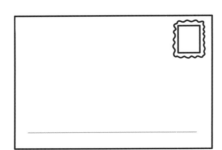

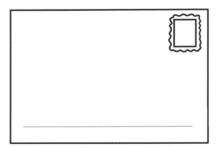

Sentences

Choose and write the best word to finish each sentence.

I brush my _____ .

fish   hair   pot

I can run and _____ .

pond   milk   jump

I see a train on the _____ .

track   groan   sport

Copy each sentence to tell the story.

 The goat jumps the gate.

_____

_____

 The goat gets a train.

_____

More sentences

Choose and colour 4 words on the grid to make your own sentence. Then write the sentence below.

I	train	can	fast.
The	clap	is	drum.
We	dog	the	hands.
Her	bang	my	jump.

_____

_____

Write about what you like to do in the park.

_____

_____

Notes for parents and carers

Topic	Teaching tip	Key vocabulary	Extension activity
CVC words: things page 4	Help your child, if needed, to use the correct starting place and letter formation for each letter.	CVC word, consonant, vowel, log, sun	Ask your child to use a finger to write CVC words on the surface of a sealed zip-lock bag full of paint.
CVC words: animals page 5	Prompt your child to say the sound for each letter as they trace or write it.	animal, fox, bat, dog, hen	Make a set of CVC animal memory cards and play a pairs matching game together.
CVC words: actions page 6	Encourage your child to use one finger for each sound in the word to help identify the missing sound.	action word, sit, run, rip, dig	Play 'Simon says' using CVC action words. Your child writes the word in the air and then does the action.
CVC words: describing words page 7	Help your child to learn the five vowels. Show how a vowel is always in the middle of a CVC word.	describing word, big, fit, wet, fun	Ask your child to write CVC describing words in rolled-out play dough using a pencil or key.
High-frequency words page 8	Tell your child to look closely at each word for a few seconds before covering it.	common, blend, segment, spell, write	Give your child magnetic letters to write each high-frequency word on the fridge for repeated practice.
Tricky words page 9	Explain that we can't sound out tricky words using simple phonics – we just have to learn them.	write, remember, understand, meaning, spell	Help your child to practise writing tricky words with fun food items – like a carrot dipped in paint.
Words with double letters page 10	Help your child to see that there is sometimes more than one possible answer – like 'miss' or 'mill'.	double, buzz, tell, hiss, puff	Read or tell the fairy tale 'The Three Little Pigs'. Help your child to write speech bubbles saying 'huff' and 'puff'.
More words with double letters page 11	Encourage your child to say each word slowly out loud before writing it down.	kiss, bull, jazz, hill, doll	Write 'kiss' on a mirror with lipstick or a whiteboard marker pen. Ask your child to write more double-letter words on the mirror.
Words with ck page 12	Remind your child that 'ck' makes a single /k/ sound and is only used in the middle or at the end of words.	kick, back, neck, ticket, duck	Ask your child to create a mind map of 'ck' words around a large 'ck', using images and writing.
Words with sh and ch page 13	Write 'kitchen' and 'fishing' to show that 'ch' and 'sh' can also be used in the middle of words.	ship, shell, chip, bench, chick	Use a simple picture dictionary together to find examples of words that begin with 'ch' and 'sh'.
Words with th and ng page 14	Remind your child about the buzzing (voiced) and whispery (unvoiced) versions of the /th/ sound (as in 'this' and 'thin').	this, thick, king, ring, sing	Challenge your child to make a long path by writing lots of 'ng' and 'th' words on a roll of masking tape.
Words with ai, ee and igh page 15	Use the words 'digraph' ("2 letters, 1 sound") and 'trigraph' ("3 letters, 1 sound") with your child.	jail, night, feet, rain, tree	Help your child to pipe 'ai', 'ee' and 'igh' words on to a cake, using icing and a piping bag.
Words with oa, oo and ar page 16	Remind your child of the long and short /oo/ sounds (as in 'moon' and 'wood').	goat, boot, tart, foot, coat	Give your child a mission to write 'oa', 'oo' and 'ar' words in moon dust (drinking chocolate powder) for aliens to read.
Words with or, ur and ow page 17	Encourage your child to read the whole sentence before working out the missing word.	fork, owl, cow, church, torch	Ask your child to write 'or', 'ur' and 'ow' words using a paintbrush and glue. Scatter glitter on top.
Words with oi, ear and air page 18	Prompt your child to think of rhyming words to help them think of additional words.	coin, beard, toilet, chair, oil	Have a chocolate-coin hunt, with 'oi', 'ear' and 'air' words on the back of them. To keep a coin, your child writes the word.

Topic	Teaching tip	Key vocabulary	Extension activity
Words with er and ure page 19	Encourage your child to try each letter on the sound buttons in turn to see if it makes a real word.	hammer, letter, otter, cure, pure	Ask your child to pick an 'er' or 'ure' word card and then write it with a toothpick in a piece of rolled-out play dough.
More high-frequency words page 20	Remind your child to look closely at all the letters in each word before writing it.	high-frequency word, common, remember, understand, meaning	Provide materials for your child to write their own set of high-frequency word cards, to help remember these words.
More tricky words page 21	Challenge your child to write the tricky words several times in each lane – repetition is the key!	tricky word, off by heart, memory, spell, spelling	Ask your child to write some tricky words in chalk outside. When they can spell a word, they can wash it away.
Captions page 22	Ask your child to talk about what happens at the beginning/middle/end of their story before they start to draw and write.	caption, label, describe, explain, comic	Encourage your child to write captions for suitable images cut out from newspapers or magazines.
Character captions page 23	Talk about the differences between what we say aloud and what we think in our heads.	speech, speech bubble, think, thought, thought bubble	Cut out card speech and thought bubbles for your child to write captions and use in role play with cuddly toys.
CVCC words: things page 24	Ask your child to name the pictures first, to help them identify the vowel sound.	CVCC word, pond, lamp, bench, chest	Challenge your child to choose one of these CVCC words and write words that rhyme with it.
CVCC words: actions page 25	Encourage your child to name the pictures before working out the missing letters.	jump, help, paint, melt, wink	Use a white crayon to write secret CVCC words, and challenge your child to reveal and read the words by brushing over the paper with watercolour paint.
CVCC words: describing words page 26	Talk about why each object can be described as 'soft' or 'fast'. Ask your child to think of other examples.	best, cold, lost, soft, fast	Give your child writing practice with alliterative descriptive phrases like 'the red rug' and 'the fit fox'.
CCVC words: things page 27	Prompt your child to say the second sound in the CCVC words clearly and separately, to avoid missing it when writing the word.	CCVC word, pram, train, flag, drum	Write vowel sounds on the ground outside in chalk and say CCVC words for your child. They must identify the vowel sound and stand on it.
CCVC words: animals page 28	Encourage your child to check their spelling of each CCVC animal name, even if it is correct.	snail, stag, crab, clam, frog	Do some internet research together about the CCVC animals. Help your child to write some key facts.
CCVC words: actions page 29	Help your child to sound out each shaded letter before working out what word they make.	step, trip, clap, drop, stop	Cut out images of CCVC actions and ask your child to write the words in shaving foam. Do this outside or on a tray.
Capital letters page 30	Show the matching lower-case letter for each capital. Help your child with the correct starting place and capital letter formation.	capital letter, lower-case letter, name, sign, information	Go on a capital-letter hunt together around your home or outside in the local area.
More capital letters page 31	Remind your child that names start with a capital letter.	sign, instruction, name, person, capital letter	Help your child to write and decorate name badges for all the members of your family.
Sentences page 32	Remind your child that sentences start with a capital letter. Point to examples on the page.	sentence, capital letter, full stop, space, story	Write simple words on construction blocks and ask your child to build their own sentences with them.
More sentences page 33	Encourage your child to put a space the size of a letter 'o' between each word in their sentences.	make up, story, sense, tell, writer	Make two giant dice with characters on one and actions on the other. Your child rolls them and writes a silly sentence.

Writing Words

Get Set Early Years

Schofield & Sims

Help children to become school-ready with **Get Set Early Years**, an engaging cross-curricular programme to bridge the gap between play and formal learning.

Developed by experienced practitioners and based on the Early Years Foundation Stage framework, **Get Set Early Years** is designed to build confidence, encourage curiosity and foster a love of learning.

- exciting and motivating activities to support classroom teaching
- friendly illustrations that children can enjoy colouring in
- key vocabulary for each topic area, providing opportunities to create a rich language environment
- notes and tips for parents and carers to help you delve further into each topic

Get Set Literacy: Writing Words develops children's ability to write simple whole words, beginning with single CVC spellings before moving on to words featuring digraphs and trigraphs, high-frequency and tricky words, and finally to captions and sentences.

Discover the other **Get Set** activity books:

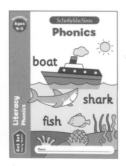

ISBN 978-07217-1444-8

ISBN 978 07217 1444 8
Early Years
Age range 4–5 years
£3.95 (Retail price)

MIX
Paper from responsible sources
FSC® C023114

For further information and to place your order visit
www.schofieldandsims.co.uk or telephone 01484 607080